I'm
on
the
Phone

Written by Greg Lang

Illustrated by Bettina Guthridge

HORWITZ
MARTIN
EDUCATION

It was time to do the dishes.
'Where are you?'
I called to my big brother.

'I'm on the phone!' he said.
'It's your turn to dry the dishes!'
I told him.

'I can't, I'm on the phone!'

We had to clean the kitchen.
Where was my big brother?
He had to sweep the floor,
but he wasn't there.

'I'm on the phone!' he said.
'But you have to do the sweeping!'
I told him.

'Leave me alone!' he said.
'I'm on the phone!'

Dad brought home the groceries.
We had to carry them in.
Where was my big brother?

'I'm on the phone!' he said.
'But you have to help!' I told him.

'Go away, I'm on the phone!'

7

We had to tidy the yard.
I couldn't find my big brother.

'I'm on the phone,' he said.
'But you have to help!' I told him.

'Not now!' he said.
'I'm on the phone!'

8

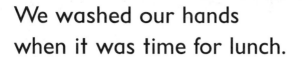

We washed our hands
when it was time for lunch.

'Where is your brother?' asked Mum.
'He's on the phone,' I said.
I called my brother.

'I'm on the phone!' he said.

Dad made a pizza and some cold drinks.
We went outside and ate our lunch.
It was great.

Then my brother came outside.
'What's for lunch?
I'm starving,' he said.
'It's all gone,' said Mum.
'But you didn't tell me!'
he said.

15

'Yes we did,' we all cried,
'but you were on the phone!'